MW01091718

Jill Rosen

Jan. 4/24

Enjoy!

ISBN: 978-1-958842-23-2
Library of Congress Control Number: 2023944367

First Published by AM Ink Publishing, Southwick, MA, 2024 AM Ink and its logos are trademarked by AM Ink Publishing.

AMInkPublishing.com

For my husband, Brian, who never wanted a third dog …
and possibly still doesn't.

Jill Rosen

Stephanie Rohr

Ode to a Pug

You're my lapdog, cuddle-bug, sweet and cute

Until you let go with a stinky pug toot

Into your pug mouth, everything goes ...

Rocks,

mud,

socks, crud,

and even my clothes

My carpets are chewed
My shoelaces frayed …
How old will you be before you obey?

When it's time to go potty, you do let me know
But just a few seconds before you must go

I am forever outside with my scoop …
Why does my tiny pug perpetually poop?

All rooms in the house stay in disarray
I am at wits end, I'm sorry to say

You don't like the heat

You don't like the cold

You snore like a geezer, 100-years-old

Yet you look so adorable in a beret …
Why, oh why, was my dog made this way?

You’re kind and polite when there’s food in your bowl
Your deep brown pug eyes touch the depths of my soul

Though once you've snarfed up the last tasty bite
You start racing around like a top wound up tight

After endless zoomies without ever a break
I'm certain there is not much more I can take

Something must change without delay
Things will only get worse if I look away

A pugnado of teeth and shedding hair
Forever ruining my favorite chair

I see you with that guilty side-eye glare
My patience is gone with none left to spare

I think my hair is about to turn gray
My nerves are so frazzled …
How can you stay?

Today is the day I will give you away!

I pick up your stuffed toys dripping with drool
You're all tuckered-out and curled up by my stool

Your snorts and your wheezes fill up my day …

BUT could I imagine it any other way?

When I give you a kiss, I smush each furry wrinkle
So soft on my skin, I don't care if you tinkle

Your tail so curly, all twisty and twirly
One of a kind, you're small but still burly

Enormous eyes, but where is your nose?
Your cute head on a tilt in that smug pug pose

In this circus of life, you are the clown
Your tongue flips up tight then zips right back down

You bark when you see a dog on TV
Or even at nothing … it's so funny to me

Your woof barely a yowl, not quite a howl
Really so silly and rarely a growl

As we near the end of each night
And you're flopped out across my legs just right

The truth is clear to my joy and dismay
I think you are perfect in every way

Today is the day I know you will stay …
Of course, I could never give you away!

But please...
Hold those stinky pug toots in ...
OKAY?

Printed in the USA
CPSIA information can be obtained
at www.ICGtesting.com
CBHW040957191023
1386CB00001B/1

9 781958 842232